MC LONGNECK'S
EPIC
SPACE
ADVENTURE

Featuring MC Longneck

and

Sputnik

his robot companion

Copyright 2015
ISBN: 978-0-578-17077-0

Andrew Rader

Illustrated by Galen Frazer

Printed in the USA
Signature Book Printing, www.sbpbooks.com

Available with companion game at www.andrew-rader.com

along with other science books & games

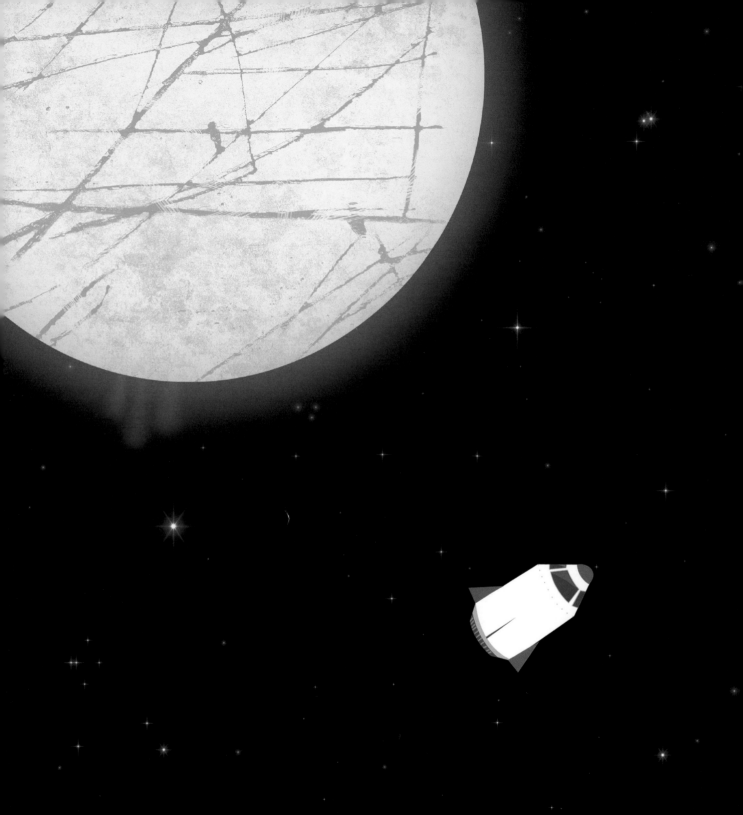

SOMEWHERE, SOMETHING INCREDIBLE IS WAITING TO BE KNOWN.
-CARL SAGAN

Attention on the pad, we're sealing up the ship! Strap in; start the countdown—we're ready for a trip!

B last off!
Engines roar with
a mighty sound.

Hold on tight,
the rocket's rising
off the ground.

C ruising through the clouds, leaving Earth behind. Up there out in space, who knows what things we'll find?

Docking at the station, we're here to re-supply. There's tons of awesome science at the lab up in the sky.

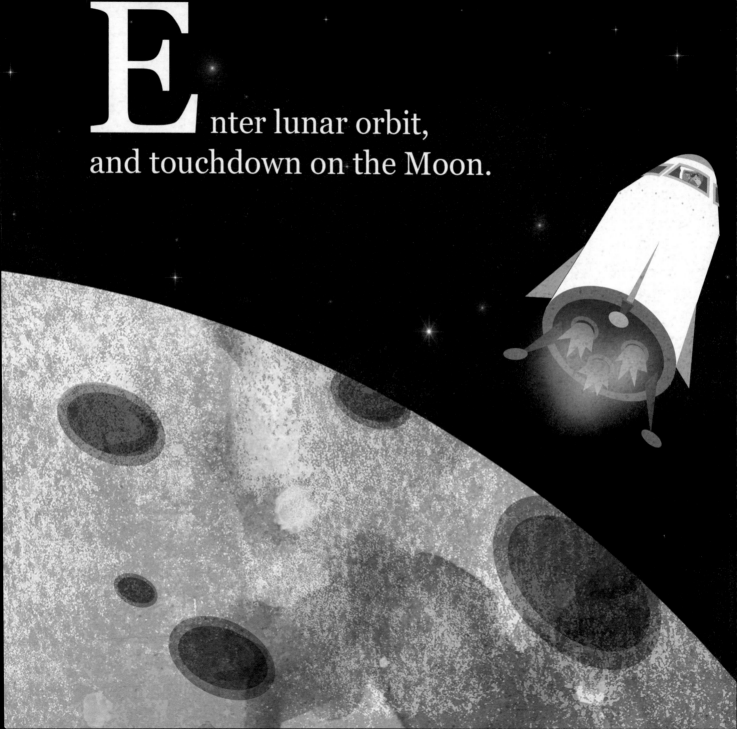

Enter lunar orbit,
and touchdown on the Moon.

Gravity's so low here, we can
jump right up that dune.

Flags, ships, and rovers lying all around. Footprints in the dust that covers the lunar ground.

Get back inside our ship, our journey's just begun!

150,000,000 KM

Flying 'cross the solar system, we're headed for the Sun.

Heat and light shining, intensely on our ship. Orbit at a distance, and continue on our trip.

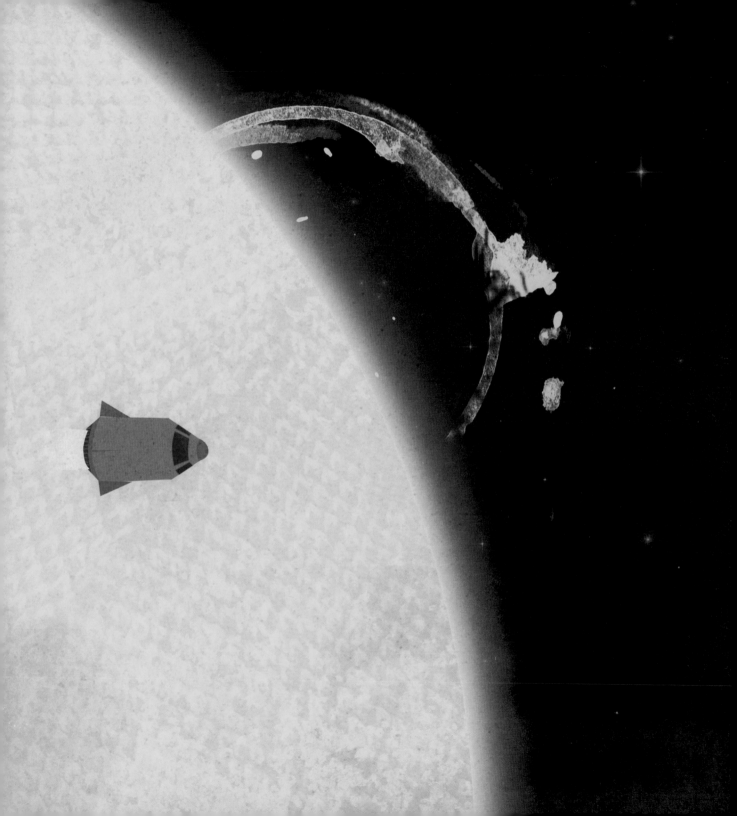

I nvestigating Mercury,
let's take a closer look.

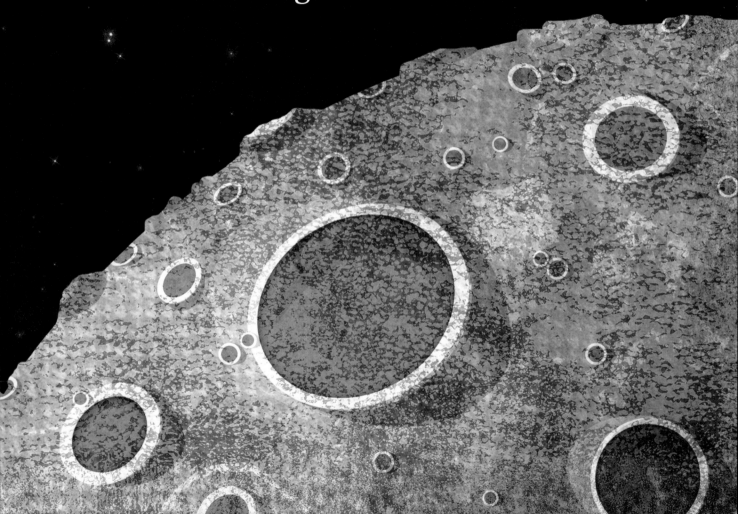

Rays streaming from the Sun,
it's hot enough to cook.

Jumping on to Venus, the hottest planet yet. That rain is made of acid, be careful - don't get wet.

K
eep the ship sealed tight,
and through the clouds we fly.

Next we're on to Mars,
that red dot in the sky.

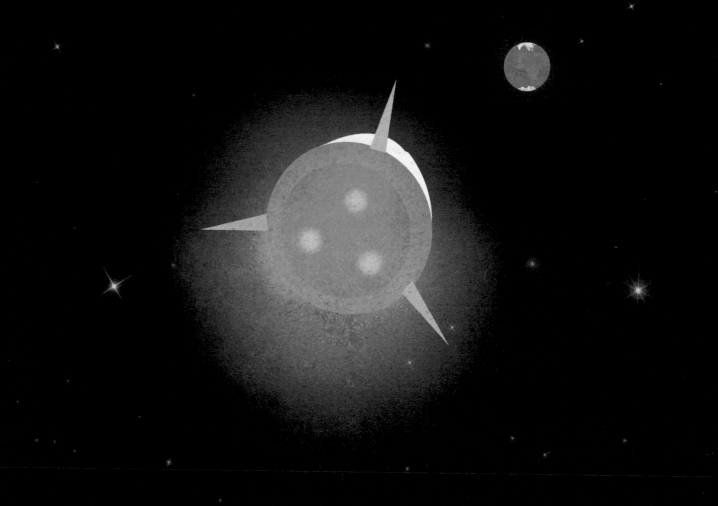

Landing is a challenge, the air is really thin. With parachute and thrusters, we touch down on our fin.

M

ars is like a desert, but one that's really cold. A whole new world before us, what secrets does it hold?

N ow climb the highest mountain, and then the valley floor.

Let's relight our rocket,
and hear the mighty roar!

One and two in orbit,
we count the moons of Mars.
Dwarfed against the planet,
small rocks among the stars.

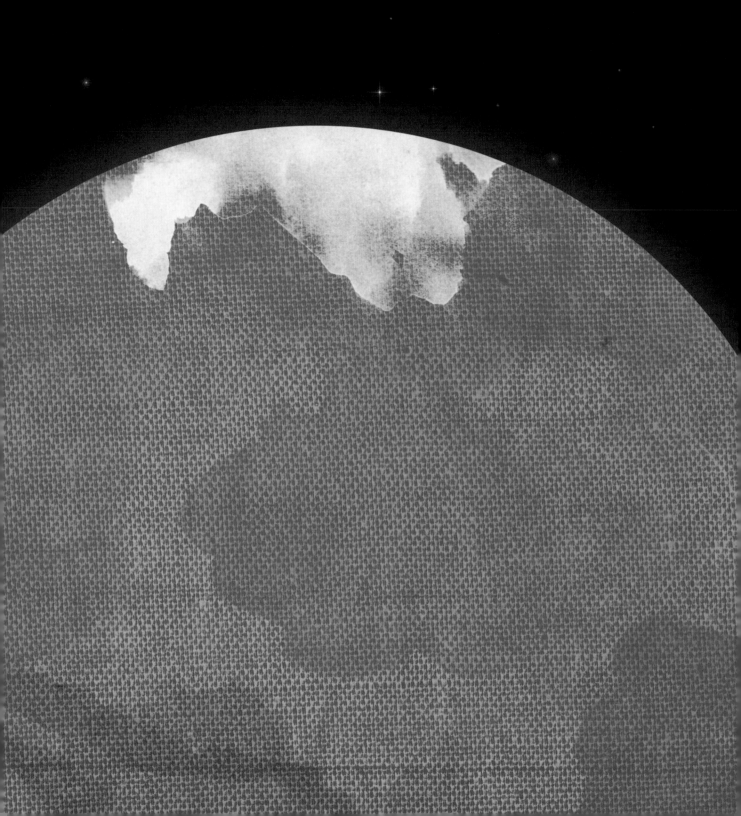

Past asteroids and comets, small worlds of ice and rock. Gravity almost nothing, you fly instead of walk.

Q uick, back into the spaceship, to Jupiter we go! The largest planet out there, with four big moons you know.

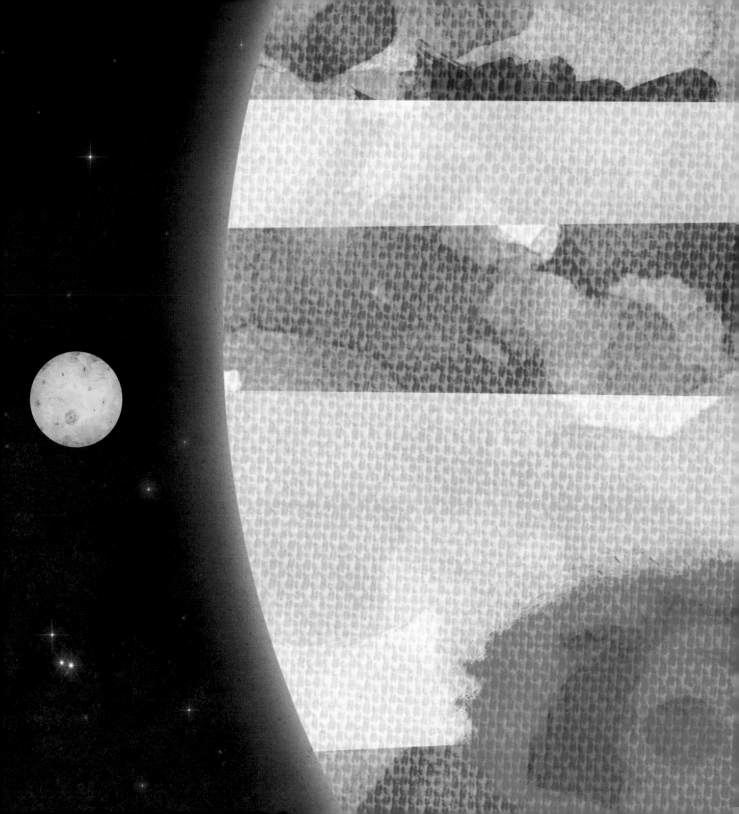

Rising plumes from Io are trailing into space.

Ice skating on Europa.
1,2,3 let's race!

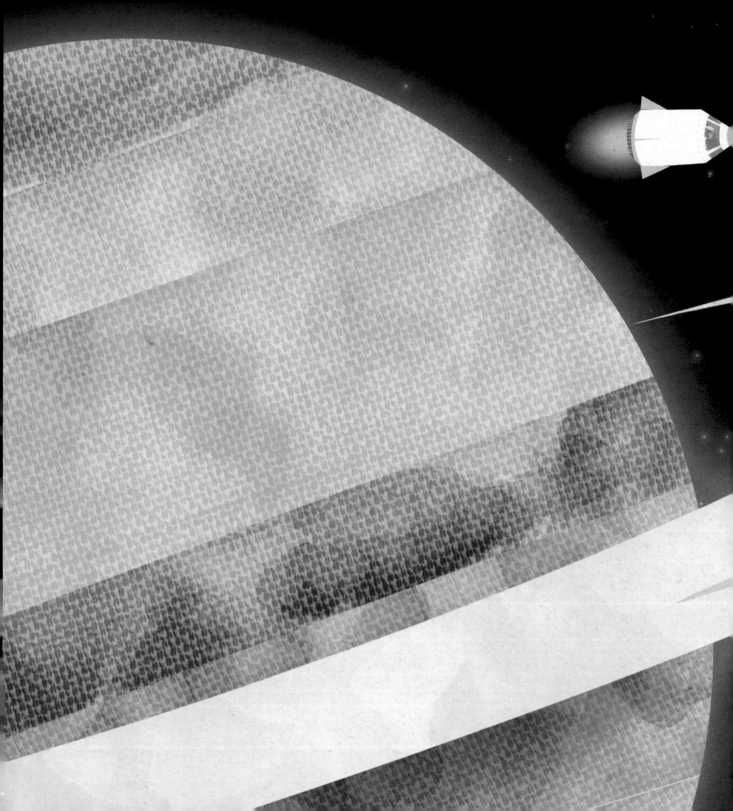

Saturn is our next stop, with over sixty moons. Clouds of gas too buoyant to even fly balloons.

Titan is the largest moon, with liquid and thick air.

You weigh so very little, you could
fly with wings you wear.

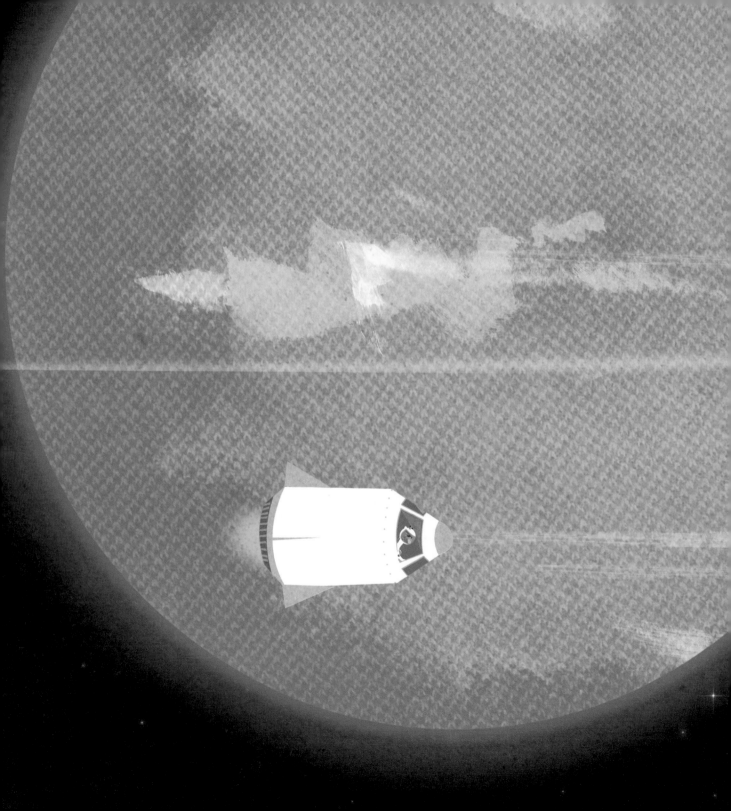

U

ranus is the next one,
with clouds of ice and gas. Ariel,
Umbriel, Miranda, we see
them through the glass.

DENSITY
2.06 G/CM

TEMP
38 K

COMPOSITION
N CH₄ H₂

Visiting mighty Neptune, we find a giant storm. We note that Triton's spin is different than the norm.

W
e're on to visit Pluto, the last stop on our flight. It's so far from the Sun that it's darker than the night.

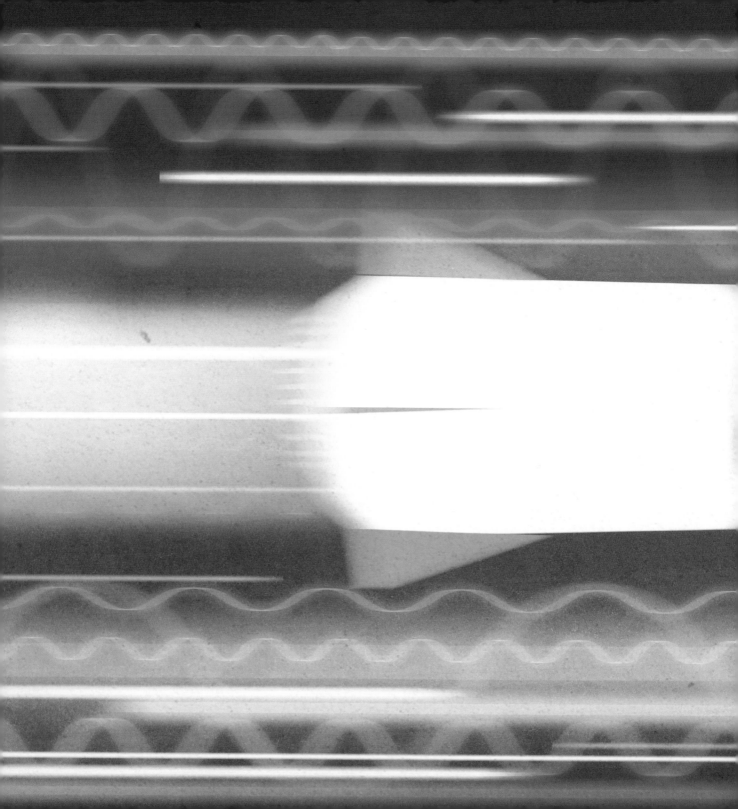

X-rays racing past us, coming from the Sun. Speeding through the Oort cloud like a bullet from a gun.

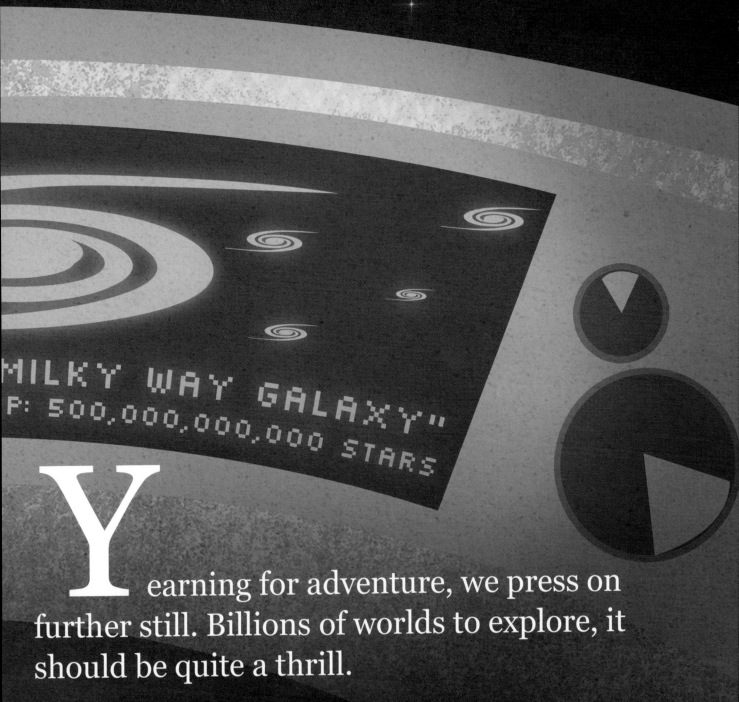

"MILKY WAY GALAXY"
P: 500,000,000,000 STARS

Yearning for adventure, we press on further still. Billions of worlds to explore, it should be quite a thrill.

Zooming through the Milky Way, take one last glance back home. We're interstellar travelers, and through the stars we roam.

Companion game at www.andrew-rader.com
along with other science books & games

 AndrewRader   @marsrader   RaderAndrew

MARS

Mars is on the edge of the habitable zone. It shares many features with Earth and may once have been covered by oceans. Mars is the only planet inhabited solely (so far as we know) by robots.

Rocky Planet
Atmosphere: Thin CO2
Radius: 0.53 x Earth
Gravity: 0.38G

MARS · PHOBOS/DEIMOS

...N ASTEROID BELT

...Mars and Jupiter are millions of ...nging from dust particles to the ...et Ceres. However, the density ...low, and numerous spacecraft ...without incident.

...BELT · CERES · VESTA

SATURN

...'s rings of ice, rock, and dust, are ...2,000 km across but less than 1 km ...proportionally thinner than a razor ...turn has over 150 identified moons, ...which have formal names.

H2/He
...arth

...S · RHEA · TITAN · IAPETUS

PLUTO

...e largest (but only second most ...iper Belt object, but it is still ...the Moon. Since its discovery ...o has only travelled a third of ...nd the Sun

...planet
...H2, CH4

...HARON · NIX

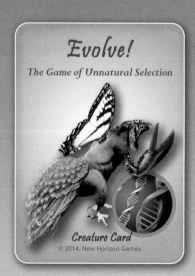

Evolve!
The Game of Unnatural Selection

Creature Card
© 2014, New Horizon Games

Mountains
Climbing, Camouflage, Survival, Insulation

Zebra Body
1 ❤ 1

Camouflage, Fast

Giraffe Head
1 · 2

...: Reaching

...eystone Species
...nning non-* challenges.